Don't Stick Up Your Nose!

Don't Stuff Stuff In Your Ears!

Jerald S. Altman, M.D. and Richard Jacobson

Don't Stick Sticks Up Your Nose!
Don't Stuff Stuff In Your Ears!
by Jerald S. Altman, M.D. and Richard Jacobson

Published by ZonaBooks, LLC

5426 East Via Los Caballos
Paradise Valley, AZ 85253

To make inquiries visit DontStickDontStuff.com

Illustrations by Brittany Clayton
Book layout by Nick Zelinger

ISBN: 978-0-9888861-3-1
LCCN: 2015901084

Printed in The United States of America

First Edition

For Every Parent, Grandparent,
Babysitter, Doctor, Nurse, Medical
Assistant, Medical Technician, Friend
Or Stranger Who Has Had To Deal
With A Scary Nasal Or Aural Insertion
By A Misguided Or Confused Child.
We Hope This Dissuades
A Few Of Them.

On your face
are choices:
your eyes, ears, mouth and nose.

When you ate your breakfast,
we all know which you chose.

No bagel in your ears,

No fried eggs up your nose.

Even though it's tempting,

That's not where breakfast goes.

Use your nose to smell things,
Do not stick sticks up there.

Don't stuff stuff in your ears,

Don't stick sticks up your nose.

That can cause such problems,

That's not where that stuff goes.

Ears have really small holes
that lead into your head.

Sounds should enter in them
and never stuff like bread!

Don't stick sticks up your nose,
Don't stuff stuff in your ears,
Finding stuff inside them,
The doctor will have fears.

Playing with your racecars?

Have fun...but this, I shout:

Toy cars up your nostrils

May never race right out.

Nurses, friends and parents,
They surely all agree:

Your ear is no place for
A buzzing bumble bee.

Don't stuff stuff in your ears,

Don't stick sticks up your nose,

That could be quite painful

Like sharp thorns on a rose.

No beehive in your ears,
No chopsticks up your nose,
Even though it's tempting,
That's not where that stuff goes.

Okay, let's consider
A warning you've not heard:
froggie up your nose, chum?
Wow! That is just absurd!

Don't stick sticks up your nose,

Don't stuff stuff in your ears,

Knowing that you've done that

May bring your Mom to tears.

Don't stuff stuff in your ears,

Don't stick sticks up your nose.

That can cause real problems,

The doctor's research shows.

You stuffed stones in your ear?
(Ouch!) That's a problem, huh?
Rocks stay on the road, pal.
Don't be meshugenah!

Don't stuff stuff in your ears,
Don't stick sticks up your nose.

Even though it's tempting,
That's not where that stuff goes.

Red pencil in your ear?
Blue crayon up your nose?

Aren't they better drawing
On paper where it shows?

No dreidel up your nose,

No shofar in your ear.

Your ears hear pretty songs.
Your nose smells yummy cake.

Keep the weird stuff out, friends,
For everybody's sake.

Don't stick sticks up your nose,

Don't stuff stuff in your ears.

Smell and listen with them.

Hip, hip, hooray! Three cheers!

The End

DontStickDontStuff.com